MEET THE SPIDER

Nice to eat you!

Though many people are scared of spiders, only a few species such as the black widow and brown recluse are harmful to humans. There are over 48,000 known species of spiders.

FAST FACTS

Most spiders are carnivores, meaning they eat meat. They catch their prey in strong, sticky webs woven from silk that comes from their body. Most spiders eat insects, but some even eat birds and lizards!

Spiders live on every continent, except Antarctica.

The smallest spiders have a body length of less than 0.015 in. (3.7 cm).

Large spiders, such as the tarantula, can reach a body length of 3.5 in. (9 cm) and a leg span of up to 9.8 in. (25 cm).

Hi! I'm a tarantula.

ANATOMY OF A SPIDER

Color the diagram below and bring the spider to life!

Dorsal view

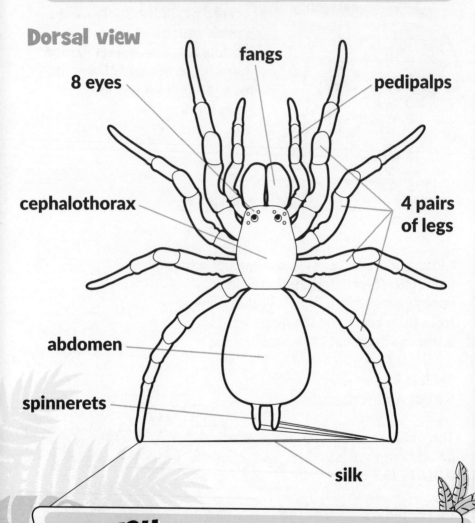

fangs

8 eyes

pedipalps

cephalothorax

4 pairs of legs

abdomen

spinnerets

silk

DID YOU KNOW?

The hairs on a spider's legs pick up vibrations and smells from the air.

CROSSWORD

Fill in the answers to all the clues.
Need a hint? Turn to the glossary at the end of the book.

Across

1. 3. 6. 7.

Down

2. 4. 5.

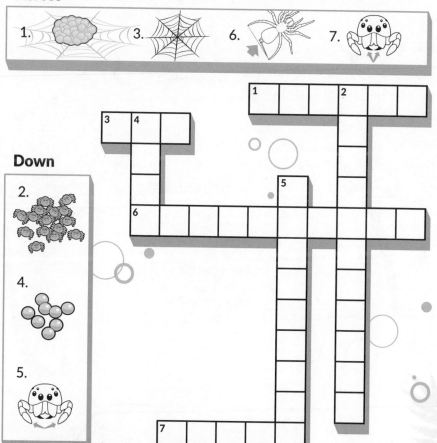

DID YOU KNOW? For its weight, spiderweb silk is five times stronger than steel.

LIFE CYCLE OF A SPIDER

There are four stages in the spider life cycle:
1) egg, 2) egg sac, 3) spiderlings, and 4) adult.

Number each stage from 1 to 4 in the circles below.

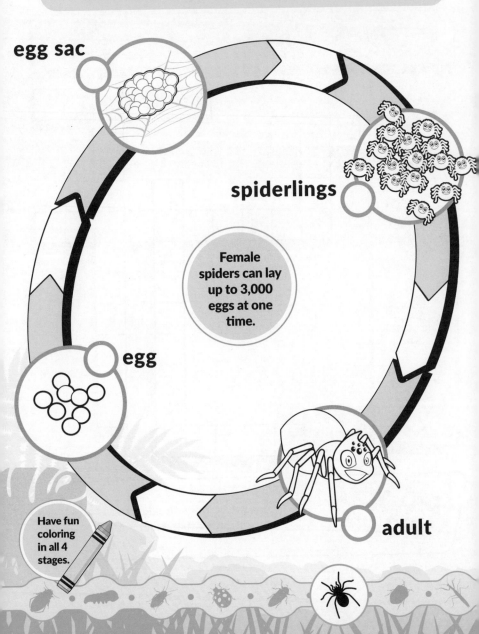

egg sac

spiderlings

Female spiders can lay up to 3,000 eggs at one time.

egg

adult

Have fun coloring in all 4 stages.

MATCH IT UP!

Draw a line from each word to the correct drawing.

 adult

 **egg sac**

 **spiderlings**

 **egg**

DINNERTIME FOR A SPIDER

What should this hungry spider have for dinner?
Color only the things it likes to eat.

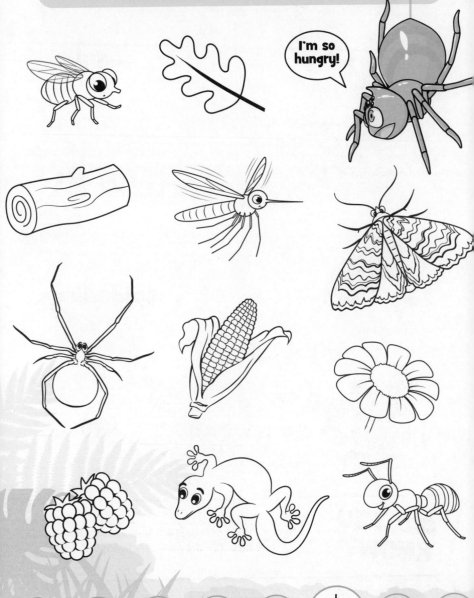

SPOT THE DIFFERENCE

Spot one difference in each picture and circle it.

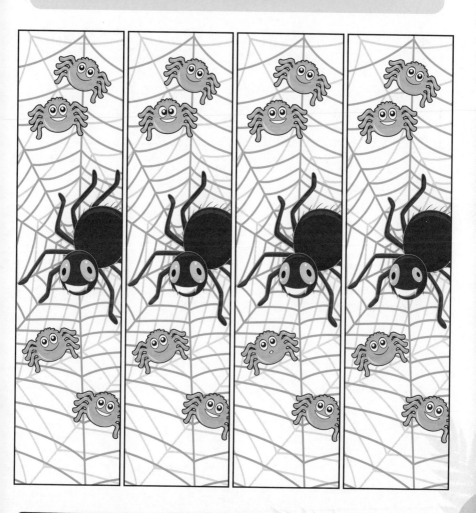

DID YOU KNOW? Spiders use their silk to climb, break their falls, create egg sacs, wrap up prey, make nests, and more.

HOW TO DRAW A SPIDER

Here are the steps to drawing a spider.

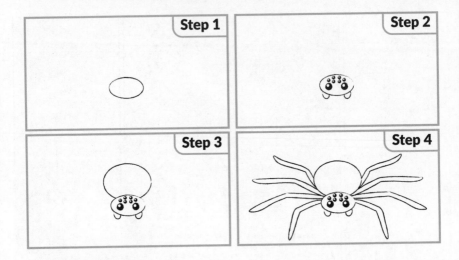

Now you try!

WORD HUNT™

Find all of the words hidden in the grid and circle them. The hidden words can be found downward ↓, forward →, or diagonally ↗ ↘.

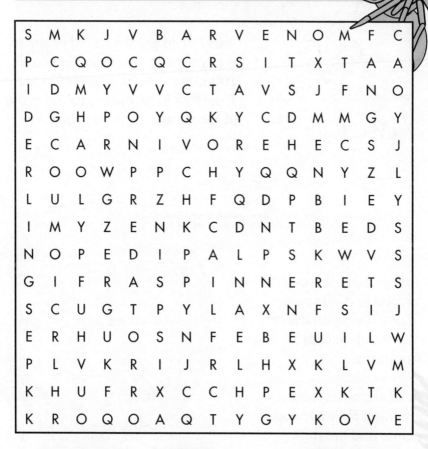

S	M	K	J	V	B	A	R	V	E	N	O	M	F	C
P	C	Q	O	C	Q	C	R	S	I	T	X	T	A	A
I	D	M	Y	V	V	C	T	A	V	S	J	F	N	O
D	G	H	P	O	Y	Q	K	Y	C	D	M	M	G	Y
E	C	A	R	N	I	V	O	R	E	H	E	C	S	J
R	O	O	W	P	P	C	H	Y	Q	Q	N	Y	Z	L
L	U	L	G	R	Z	H	F	Q	D	P	B	I	E	Y
I	M	Y	Z	E	N	K	C	D	N	T	B	E	D	S
N	O	P	E	D	I	P	A	L	P	S	K	W	V	S
G	I	F	R	A	S	P	I	N	N	E	R	E	T	S
S	C	U	G	T	P	Y	L	A	X	N	F	S	I	J
E	R	H	U	O	S	N	F	E	B	E	U	I	L	W
P	L	V	K	R	I	J	R	L	H	X	K	L	V	M
K	H	U	F	R	X	C	C	H	P	E	X	K	T	K
K	R	O	Q	O	A	Q	T	Y	G	Y	K	O	V	E

ARACHNID   FANGS   SPINNERETS
CARNIVORE   PEDIPALPS   SILK
EYES   PREDATOR   VENOM
               SPIDERLINGS

MEET THE ANT!

It's a pleasure to meet you!

Ants have walked the earth on tiny legs for 130 million years. That's right—they once lived with dinosaurs!

Ants live in groups called colonies that range in size from less than 100 members to over a million. They live in an underground group of rooms and tunnels called a nest.

FAST FACTS

Today, there are over 12,000 known species of ants living on every continent, except Antarctica.

Ants are omnivores—meaning they eat both plants and meat.

They range in size from 0.03 in. (0.75 mm) to 2.4 in. (6 cm).

Let me amaze you with my feats of strength!

ANATOMY OF AN ANT

Color the diagrams below and bring the ant to life!

Dorsal view

antennae

head

thorax

abdomen

Side view

mandibles

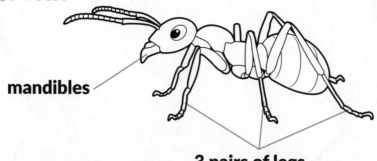

3 pairs of legs

DID YOU KNOW? Ants have two stomachs—one to store food for themselves—and another, called the "social" stomach, to store food for other ants.

LIFE CYCLE OF AN ANT

There are four stages in the life cycle of an ant:
1) egg, 2) larva, 3) pupa, and 4) adult.

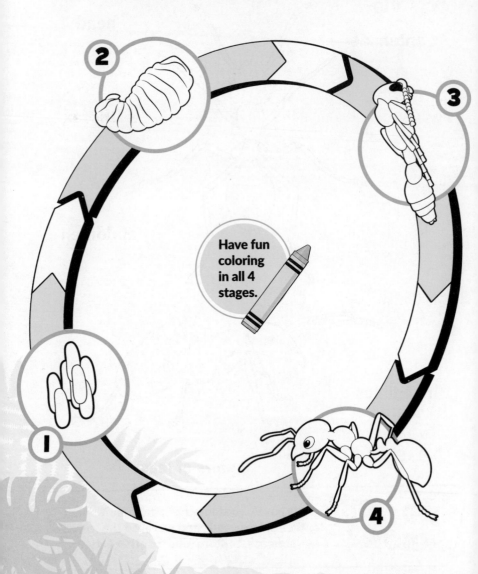

Have fun coloring in all 4 stages.

MATCH IT UP!

Draw a line from each word to the correct drawing.

 larva

 adult

 egg

 pupa

SEARCH & FIND

Can you find the following?

 **1 QUEEN**   **8 WORKERS**   **2 MALES**   **20 EGGS**   **11 LARVAE**

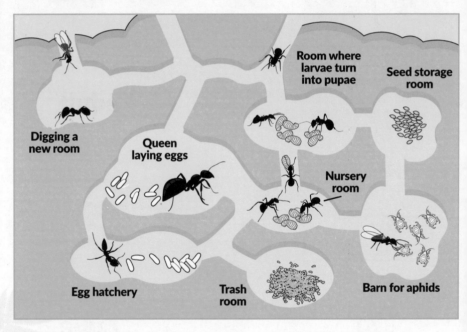

Digging a new room

Room where larvae turn into pupae

Seed storage room

Queen laying eggs

Nursery room

Egg hatchery

Trash room

Barn for aphids

Ant colonies are made up of queens, workers, and males. Each group does a different job.

QUEEN:
- Larger than the worker ants
- Lays eggs
- Has wings that fall off after finding a new nest

WORKER:
- Female
- Can't lay eggs
- No wings
- Raises young
- Builds nest
- Gathers food

MALE (DRONE):
- Has wings
- Doesn't work in the nest
- Mates with queen, then dies

THE FARTHEST TRAVELER

Add up the numbers below each ant to find which one traveled the farthest. Write the totals in the boxes.

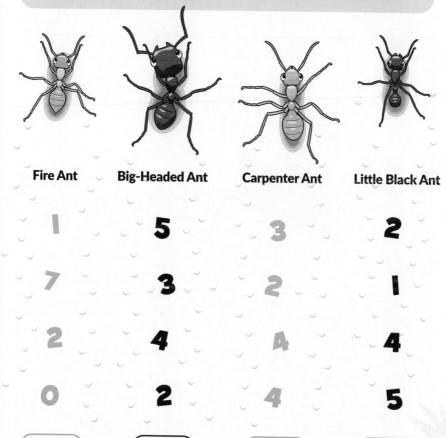

Fire Ant	Big-Headed Ant	Carpenter Ant	Little Black Ant
1	5	3	2
7	3	2	1
2	4	4	4
0	2	4	5

A-MAZE-ING ANTHILL

Help Herbert the Ant reunite with his friend Lulu inside the anthill.

WORD JUMBLE

Unscramble each jumble and write the word on the lines below.

OYLNCO

KROEWR

_____

_____

EQNEU

RNDOE

_____

_____

SIMEBNLAD

ALVRA

_____

_____

ENLUNT

VMEIONOER

_____

_____

MAKE YOUR OWN ANT FARM!

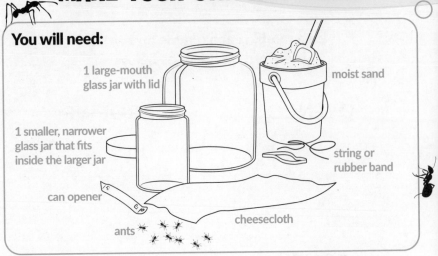

You will need:

1 large-mouth glass jar with lid

moist sand

1 smaller, narrower glass jar that fits inside the larger jar

string or rubber band

can opener

cheesecloth

ants

Step 1

Add a 1-in. (2.5-cm) layer of moist sand to the bottom of the large jar.

Step 2

Find an anthill and catch a few ants in the smaller jar. Make sure they are not red ants.

Step 3

Place the small jar upside down on the sand layer in the larger jar.

Step 4

Fill the space between the two jars with moist sand.

Step 5

Use the can opener to poke holes in the lid. Place the lid back on the jar. Cover with lid with cheesecloth and secure with string or a rubber band.

CARING FOR YOUR ANTS

Light: Do not place your farm in a window or under a lamp. Give it indirect sunlight only.

Water: Mist the inside of the jar and sand regularly to keep things moist—just enough to dampen the sand. You don't want to drown the ants.

Food: Feed your ants once every 6 hours. Add some breadcrumbs soaked in sugar water and small pieces of fruit. If they don't eat it all, give them less next time.
Ants need protein such as dead crickets, flies, mealworms, wax worms. You can buy these at a pet store.

Drink: Mix 7 parts water to 1 part sugar or honey. Pour some into a pop bottle cap and put it in the jar.

REMEMBER: Only keep the ants in your farm for a few days. Release them back where you found them.

SPIKER V

SCARIEST

SPIDER

Arachnophobia—the unreasonable fear of spiders—is one of the most common phobias.

ANT

Have you ever heard of myrmecophobia? This lesser-known phobia is an unreasonable fear of ants.

 **‹‹‹ WINNER**

STRONGEST

SPIDER

Some spiders can carry birds and fish.

The jumping spider can carry 170 times its body weight.

ANT

Some ants can lift 50 times their body weight.

They work together to carry large objects.

Relative to their size, ants are among the strongest creatures in the world.

 WINNER ›››

S. ANT

MOST ARTISTIC

SPIDER

Spiders produce up to eight types of silk for different tasks, such as weaving webs and bundling prey.

Different species of spiders weave different types of web, including spiral orbwebs and sheet webs.

ANT

Ants make complex systems of tunnels and rooms underground.

Human artists sometimes cast these underground networks in plaster and show them in galleries.

 **《《 WINNER**

TEAM WORKER

SPIDER

Most spiders live, raise their young, and capture prey all by themselves.

In rare cases, spiders will work together to build a large communal web to capute prey.

ANT

Ants work together to raise young, build the nest, and collect food. They even have a second stomach to bring food for other ants.

Ants gather in groups to carry large food items and solve problems.

 WINNER 》》

BUILD A BUG

STEP 1: PLAN

Your insect should include the following:

○ head   ○ 6 legs (3 pairs)
○ thorax   ○ antennae
○ abdomen   ○ eyes

Optional: wings

What insects inspire you?

_____

What attributes will your insect have?

_____

STEP 2: DESIGN

Practice drawing
your insect here:

STEP 3: ENGINEER

Suggested materials:	What else could you use?
clay pipe cleaners toothpicks	_____ _____ _____

Now it's time to follow your plan and build your insect!

STEP 4: REVIEW

How did your insect model turn out?

Great   Okay   Not Great

What parts of the model worked well?

_____
_____

What challenges did you have?

_____
_____
_____

Is there anything you would do differently next time?

_____
_____
_____
_____

INSECT GLOSSARY

abdomen - One of the three main body segments of insects. It contains the heart, the midgut, the digestive system, and the reproductive organs.

antenna (plural: antennae) - Sensory organs on the head of insects.

carnivore - An organism that mostly eats meat.

colony - A group of ants including queens, workers, and drones.

dorsal - The upper surface of an organism.

herbivore - An organism that mostly eats plants.

larva (plural: larvae) - A juvenile form of an insect that looks different from the adult.

mandible - Part of an insect's mouth used for biting or cutting.

nocturnal - Animals that are mostly active at night.

omnivore - An organism that eats plants and meat.

predator - An animal that eats other animals.

pupa - The third stage in the life cycle of insects undergoing metamorphosis.

spinneret - An organ of the spider that produces silk.

Editor: Erika Szucs | Writer: Megan Faulkner
Proofreaders: Clarissa Sorgiovanni, Diandra D'Alessio
Art Director: Tammy Desnoyers | Graphic Designers: Rafaela Petel Ruiz, Robert Nikolakakis
Illustration: Robert Nikolakakis, Tim Murray, Freepik.com and Shutterstock.com

We acknowledge the financial support of the Government of Canada.

 Government of Canada   Gouvernement du Canada   Canada

ANSWERS

CROSSWORD

LIFE CYCLE OF A SPIDER

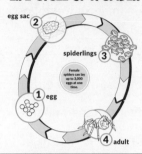

egg sac 2

spiderlings 3

Female spiders can lay up to 3,000 eggs at one time.

1 egg

4 adult

SPIDER MATCH IT UP!

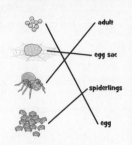

adult

egg sac

spiderlings

egg

DINNERTIME FOR A SPIDER

I'm so happy

SPOT THE DIFFERENCE

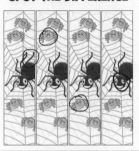

WORD HUNT™

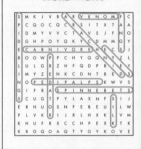

ANT MATCH IT UP!

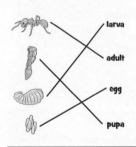

larva

adult

egg

pupa

THE FARTHEST TRAVELER

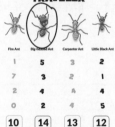

Fire Ant	Big-headed Ant	Carpenter Ant	Little Black Ant
1	5	3	2
7	3	2	1
2	4	4	4
0	2	4	5
10	**14**	**13**	**12**

A-MAZE-ING ANTHILL

WORD JUMBLE

OYLNCO
colony

KROEWR
worker

EQNEU
queen

RNDOE
drone

SIMEBNLAD
mandibles

ALVRA
larva

ENLUNT
tunnel

VMEIONOER
omnivore